Battlefield of the Mind
Study Guide

Winning the Battle in Your Mind

by
Joyce Meyer

Harrison House
Tulsa, Oklahoma

Battlefield of the Mind Study Guide –
Winning the Battle in Your Mind
ISBN 1-57794-502-6
(Previously ISBN 1-57794-185-3)
Copyright © 2000 by Joyce Meyer
Life In The Word, Inc.
P. O. Box 655
Fenton, Missouri 63026

Published by Harrison House, Inc.
P. O. Box 35035
Tulsa, Oklahoma 74153

06 05 04 03 02   28 27 26 25 24 23 22 21 20 19 18 17 16 15 14 13 12 11 10 9 8 7 6

Contents

PART 1

The Importance of the Mind

Introduction

The Bible makes it clear that the mind is the leader or forerunner of all actions. Proverbs 23:7 tells us: "For as he" [a person] "thinks in his heart, so is he...." (Also see Romans 8:5.)

If we renew our mind according to God's Word, we will, as Romans 12:2 promises, prove for ourselves "what is the good and acceptable and perfect will of God" for our lives. If we think and dwell on negative thoughts, we will have a negative life.

God wants us to experience the fullness of life He sent Jesus to provide for all those who believe in Him and receive it; Satan wants to stop us from receiving all that God has for us. Because our actions are a direct result of our thoughts, Satan's strategy is to wage war against us in our minds by bombarding us with thoughts contrary to the truth of God's Word. He wants to deceive us into believing damaging patterns of untrue thoughts, or strongholds, that we will allow to influence our lives and hold us in bondage.

The battlefield is the mind, and 2 Corinthians 10:4,5 describes the weapons of warfare God has given us "for the overthrow and destruction of strongholds." This study guide describes how to use those weapons.

USING THIS STUDY GUIDE

The purpose of this workbook is to reinforce the principles taught in my book, *Battlefield of the Mind*. You will need a copy of *Battlefield of the Mind* to work through this book.

This study guide is written in a question and answer format. By reading a chapter in *Battlefield of the Mind,* the designated Scripture verses, then answering the questions in the corresponding chapter of the study guide, you will gain a deeper understanding of the principles and learn more easily how to incorporate them into your daily life.

To use this workbook, look up the corresponding chapter in *Battlefield of the Mind* and read it. Next look up in your Bible the Scriptures designated in the study guide and read them. This is an important step because those Scriptures are the basis of the teaching in that particular chapter and are taken directly from that chapter.

Answer the questions in the study guide by referring to the appropriate chapter in *Battlefield of the Mind.* Once you have finished answering the questions in each chapter, turn to the answer key in the back of this book to check your answers.

1. Work at a comfortable pace. Don't rush to finish quickly. Stay in each chapter until you have a thorough understanding of the material and how it pertains to your life.

2. Follow these steps with each chapter in this study guide.

3. Use this study guide for individual study or group discussion. When using it in a group, discuss your answers and learn how to apply the principles in a way that may not have occurred to you until you heard the experiences of others.

Consistently and steadily working through this book will help you renew your mind to God's Word. You will find that your pattern of thinking is gradually transforming from wrong, negative thoughts into God-like thoughts. Changing your way of thinking will enable you to change things in your life that you thought you would have to live with forever.

WALK IN GOD'S GOOD PLAN FOR YOU

Lining up our thoughts with God's thoughts is vital to overcoming negative thoughts from Satan and brings freedom and peace. We must know God's Word well enough to be able to compare what is in our mind with what is in the mind of God; any thought that attempts to exalt itself above the Word of God we are to cast down and bring into captivity to Jesus Christ. This process takes time.

I believe the God-directed, God-empowered principles in this study guide are important tools that will help you to achieve this goal. I want to encourage you to study and meditate on them; then apply what you learn to your life and allow the Holy Spirit to enlighten the eyes of your spirit (which is your heart) with God's wisdom and revelation. As you do, I believe you will see great results in winning the war that Satan has launched and ensure your victory in the battlefield of the mind.

If you are one of millions of people who suffer from worry, doubt, confusion, depression, anger or condemnation, you are experiencing an attack in your mind. But you don't have to live your whole life like this! Satan offers wrong thinking to everyone, but you do not have to accept his offer.

I pray that working through this study guide, along with the book, *Battlefield of the Mind,* will help firmly establish in your heart forever that you need to begin to think about what you are thinking about, so that you line up your thoughts with God's thoughts. This renewal of the mind is a process that requires time, but it is well worth the effort. For when you begin to see God's good plan for you in your thinking, you will begin to walk in it.

1. Read 2 Corinthians 10:4,5; Proverbs 23:7 KJV

    Why are our thoughts important? _Our thoughts are important because knowledge is the weapon used against satans meanness and they bring us closer to God_

2. Read Romans 8:5

    How do our actions relate to our thoughts? _What we think is how we live. If you always think of all things you want that is what you work for, if you think about all God wants for us - that is the direction_

3. Read Romans 12:2 _we live_

    How will our lives be changed if we renew our minds according to God's Word? _We'd be free from the world, happy_

    _____

    _____

    _____

4. Review 2 Corinthians 10:4,5

    How will we know the difference between what is in our mind and what is the mind of God? _God is good + loving We usually think thoughts like I'm stupid, I can't do it God wants us to have good thoughts_

The Mind Is the Battlefield

In the original book, *Battlefield of the Mind*, read Chapter 1, then read in your Bible the Scriptures designated below and answer the questions that follow. When you finish, check your answers in the answer key provided at the end of this book.

As you continue to follow this procedure throughout this workbook, you can be assured that you will gain insight through understanding that will help you integrate these godly principles into your daily life and win the battle in your mind!

1. Read Ephesians 6:12; John 8:44

    a. How does Satan attempt to defeat us? by feeding us lies

    .

    b. What did Jesus call the devil? father of lies

    .

    c. In what way does Satan try to bombard our minds to defeat us? by taking things that have happened to us & say things to us over & over.

    d. Explain the phrase: "One of the devil's strong points is patience." He wants to win, so he will just keep at you day after day waiting to destroy you.

2. Read 2 Corinthians 10:4,5

    a. What are "strongholds," and how does Satan attempt to set them up in our mind? _____

_____

_____ .

   b. Read the examples of strongholds Mary and John encountered in the text and give an example of a stronghold you have struggled with in your life. _____

_____

_____ .

   c. How might this stronghold have come about? _____

_____

_____

_____ .

3. Read John 8:31,32; Mark 4:24

   a. How can we overcome strongholds? _____

_____

_____

_____ .

   b. How are we to use the weapon of the Word of God to overcome strongholds? _____

_____

_____ .

   c. Why are prayer and praise effective weapons in overcoming strongholds? _____

_____

_____

_____ .

God never loses a battle. He has a definite battle plan — and when we follow it, we always win! Praise and worship are really a battle position! They confuse the enemy. When we take our position, we will see the enemy's defeat!

4. Read Luke 4:18,19

   a. According to this passage, what has God promised concerning the poor, the captives, the blind, the oppressed and others? _____

   _____

   _____

   _____.

   b. What can John and Mary (in the text) do that will set them free from their conflicting problems? _____

   _____

   _____.

5. Read 1 Corinthians 10:13

   What does this verse say about God and the temptations and trials we encounter while tearing down strongholds? _____

   _____

   _____.

Chapter

2

A Vital Necessity

As with the previous chapter, before answering the questions below, first read the corresponding chapter in *Battlefield of the Mind* then the Scriptures designated below. After you complete the chapter, check the answer key in the back of this book.

To gain the greatest benefit from this workbook, continue using this method throughout.

1. Read Proverbs 23:7

   This Scripture shows us how very important it is that we think properly. The first paragraph of *Battlefield of the Mind*, Chapter 2, tells us thoughts are _____, and according to the writer of the book of Proverbs, they have _____.
   Explain what this statement means: _____
   _____
   _____.

2. Read Romans 8:5

   a. To have a successful Christian life, what alternative to fleshly, wrong and negative thoughts is a vital necessity? _____
   _____
   _____.

   b. If your life is in a state of chaos because of years of wrong thinking, what can you do to straighten it out? _____
   _____
   _____.

3. Read Zechariah 4:6

   a. Since determination is not enough to be set free from strong-holds, what else is needed? _____
   _____
   _____ .

   b. In what way is right thinking compared to a heartbeat or blood pressure? _____
   _____
   _____ .

4. Read Matthew 12:33

   a. Explain how the phrase "a tree is known by its fruit" pertains to our lives. _____
   _____
   _____ .

   b. Can a person's thought life be discerned by looking at his attitude toward life in general? Explain. _____
   _____
   _____ .

Chapter
3

Don't Give Up!

1. Read Galatians 6:9

    How can you regain territory you have lost to the devil?_____

    _____

    _____ .

2. Read Isaiah 43:2

    a. What does God promise us regarding difficulties we experience?

        _____

        _____ .

    b. Quitting is easy. How can we overcome difficulties?_____

        _____

        _____ .

3. Read Deuteronomy 30:19; Proverbs 18:21

    a. How can we decide what is right or wrong for us on a daily basis?

        _____

        _____ .

    b. How can we avoid choosing death? _____

        _____

        _____ .

4. Read Deuteronomy 1:2,6-8

    a. Why did it take the Israelites forty years to make an eleven-day journey? How does their problem relate to us today in our spiritual journey? _____

_____

_____ .

b. When God told the Israelites, "You have dwelt long enough on this mountain," what was He really saying? What is He saying to us today?_____

_____

_____

_____ .

As we renew our minds with the Word of God, we will begin to see positive changes in our thoughts and in all other areas of life!

Chapter
4

Little by Little

1. Read Deuteronomy 7:22

    a. The process of renewing our minds takes place _____ .

    b. Why did God tell the Israelites He would clear out their enemies this way? _____
    _____
    _____ .

    c. What is the "beast" that will consume us if we receive too much freedom too quickly? _____
    _____
    _____ .

2. Read 1 Peter 5:10

    Why do we need to suffer "a little while"? _____
    _____
    _____ .

3. Read Romans 8:1

    a. What can we learn from watching a baby's attempts to walk? ___
    _____
    _____
    _____ .

    b. How does the devil try to stop you from renewing your mind? What can you do to stop his attempts? _____
    _____

_____

_____ .

c. Walking after the flesh is _____

_____ .

d. Walking after the Spirit is _____

_____ .

e. When you fail, that doesn't mean you are a failure. What does it mean? _____

_____

_____ .

4. Read Psalm 42:5; James 1:4 KJV; Philippians 1:6; 2:13

a. What happens to hope and victory when we become discouraged? _____

_____

_____ .

b. What should you do to overcome condemnation and discouragement? _____

_____

_____

_____ .

Chapter
5

Be Positive

1. Read Matthew 8:13

   Explain the effect of positive and negative thoughts on the lives of people. _____

   _____

   _____ .

2. Read Romans 8:28; 12:16

   a. Does the Bible say that all things are good?_____

      _____

      _____ .

   b. How are we to react when our plans don't work out? _____

      _____

      _____ .

3. Read 2 Corinthians 5:17

   Many of us have had bad things happen to us, things which cause us to be negative about the future. According to this verse, how should we react to such situations? _____

   _____

   _____

   _____ .

4. Read John 16:7,8; Philippians 1:6

   a. Why did Jesus say it was "profitable" for us that He go away? ____

      _____

      _____ .

b. What does Jesus teach us that the Holy Spirit will do for us? __

_____

_____ .

c. What does the Bible say about the work God has begun in us?

_____

_____ .

You may not be able to resist the sin of speaking negatively, but when you do, ask God to help you. Speaking negatively about yourself will hinder the good things God has for you.

5. Read Acts 17:11 KJV

How can we achieve balance in our thinking? _____

_____

_____ .

6. Read Romans 4:18-20; Hebrews 6:19

a. Being positive does not mean that we are to ignore the obvious. How do we deal with impossible situations without losing hope?

_____

_____ .

b. What is the anchor of the soul? How does it help us? _____

_____

_____ .

7. Read Isaiah 30:18; Proverbs 15:15

a. What is God's desire toward us as reflected in these passages? What do we need to do to receive His will for us? _____

_____

_____ .

  b. What are "evil forebodings"? How are we to deal with them? __

_____

_____ .

8. Read 1 Peter 3:10

    What does this verse say we must do if we want to enjoy life and see
    good days? _____

_____

_____ .

Mind-Binding Spirits

1. Read Philippians 4:6,7 KJV

   How can we experience the peace of God? _____
   _____
   _____
   _____
   _____.

2. Read John 8:31,32; Psalm 107:20

   How can we overcome "mind-binding spirits"? _____
   _____
   _____.

3. Read Romans 8:26; James 1:2-8

   a. As Christians, why must we decide to believe? How can we
      believe during times when our minds don't understand every-
      thing? _____
      _____.

   b. What should we do when we are going through trials? _____
      _____
      _____
      _____.

Chapter 7

Think About What You're Thinking About

1. Read Psalm 119:15; Psalm 1:3

    What are we to spend our time thinking about or meditating on? How will this benefit us?_____

    _____

    _____.

2. Read Mark 4:24

    a. What does this statement tell us: "The more time we spend thinking about the Word we read and hear, the more power and ability we will have to do it — the more revelation knowledge we will have about what we have read or heard"? _____

    _____

    _____.

    b. Why aren't most Christians living victorious lives? _____

    _____

    _____.

3. Read Psalm 1:1,2; Proverbs 4:20

    a. How do we attend to God's Word? _____

    _____

    _____.

    b. How does the old saying "practice makes perfect" pertain to Christianity? _____

    _____

_____

_____.

4. Read Joshua 1:8

    a. If you want to be successful and prosper in all your dealings, the Bible says you must _____

    _____

    _____.

    b. How does the devil control people's lives? _____

    _____.

5. Read Ephesians 2:3

    a. The Apostle Paul warns us that we are not to be governed by _____ or to obey _____

    _____.

    b. Why must we think about what we are thinking about? _____

    _____.

6. Read Psalm 48:9; Psalm 143:4,5

    a. What was King David's response to his feelings of depression and gloom? _____

    _____

    _____.

    b. What role does our mind play in our victory? _____

    _____

    _____

_____

_____ .

7. Read Romans 12:2

    a. Why is renewing our minds so vital? _____

    _____ .

    b. To what should our minds be renewed? _____

    _____ .

8. Read Philippians 4:8

    a. Why are we instructed to think on good things? _____

    _____ .

    b. How does Satan deceive people as to the source of their misery?

    _____

    _____

    _____ .

    c. How can thinking about what you are thinking about help you?

    _____

    _____ .

PART 2

Conditions of the Mind

Introduction

*H*ave you noticed that the condition of your mind changes? One time you may be calm and peaceful, and another time anxious and worried. Or you may make a decision and be sure about it, then later find your mind in a confused condition concerning the very thing you were previously so clear and certain about.

Because it seems that the mind can be in so many different conditions, it is helpful to know when our minds are normal. That way we can learn to deal with abnormal thinking patterns immediately upon their arrival.

Our minds are not born again with the New Birth experience — they have to be renewed. (Romans 12:2.) Satan will aggressively fight against the renewal of our minds, but it is vital that we press on and continue to pray and study in this area until we gain measurable victory. I believe this next section of the guidebook will open your eyes to normal and abnormal mindsets for the believer who has determined to walk in victory.

1. Read 1 Corinthians 2:16

    a. According to this Scripture, what do we as believers "hold" when we have "the mind of Christ"? _____
    _____ .

    b. Give an example of the kind of mind that should be considered abnormal for a believer. _____
    _____
    _____ .

2. Read Romans 12:2

   Are our minds reborn with the New Birth experience? Why or why not? _____

   _____ .

3. Read 1 Peter 5:7

   Are our minds supposed to wander or be upset, confused, full of doubt and unbelief, or anxious, worried and tormented by fear? Why or why not? _____

   _____

   _____ .

When Is My Mind Normal?

1. Read Ephesians 1:17,18

   a. What does the phrase "the eyes of the heart" describe? _____
   _____ .

   b. Explain the principle of "the mind aiding the spirit."_____
   _____ .

2. Read 1 Corinthians 2:11

   a. What comparison can be made between a person's own spirit and
   the Holy Spirit? _____
   _____
   _____
   _____ .

   b. What is one of the purposes of the Holy Spirit? _____
   _____ .

   c. How is this purpose of the Holy Spirit accomplished? _____
   _____
   _____ .

   d. Why does the Holy Spirit function this way? _____
   _____
   _____ .

   e. Why is it important that our minds be enlightened concerning
   what is going on in our spirits? _____
   _____ .

3. Read 1 Kings 19:11,12 KJV

    How does God speak to us most of the time? _____

    _____ .

4. Read 1 Corinthians 14:15

    How did Paul say he prayed? _____

    _____ .

5. Read 1 Corinthians 14:13,14

    How does praying in the spirit and interpretation of tongues illus-
    trate the principle of "mind aiding spirit"? _____

    _____

    _____ .

6. Read Isaiah 26:3

    a. Why does the devil want to overload and overwork your mind by
        filling it with every kind of wrong thought? _____

        _____

        _____ .

    b. What condition should the mind be in? _____

        _____ .

A Wandering, Wondering Mind

1. Read 1 Peter 1:13 KJV

   a. What does an inability to concentrate indicate? _____

   _____ .

   b. What are some of the causes of an inability to concentrate? ___

   _____ .

   c. What is the difference between a lack of comprehension and a lack of concentration? _____

   _____

   _____

   _____ .

2. Read Ecclesiastes 5:1

   a. What does the expression "keep your foot" mean? What is it a warning against? _____

   _____

   _____ .

   b. Give an example from your own life of a wandering mind. _____

   _____

   _____

   _____

   _____ .

   c. How do you correct a wandering mind? _____

   _____ .

3. Mark 11:23,24

   a. What is wrong with wondering?_____

      _____

      _____

      _____ .

   b. As Christians, we are to _____ — not doubt or wonder.

A Confused Mind

1. Read James 1:5-8

    Why are wondering, doubt and confusion undesirable activities for us as Christians? _____

    _____

    _____ .

2. Read Matthew 16:8 KJV

    a. Why are a large percentage of God's people admittedly confused?

        _____

        _____ .

    b. What is "reasoning"? _____

        _____ .

    c. Why shouldn't we rely on reasoning when God directs us to do something? _____

        _____

        _____

        _____ .

3. Read 1 Corinthians 2:14 KJV

    a. What is the Christian alternative to reasoning in the mind? ___

        _____

        _____ .

    b. Give an example from your own life of a struggle between the carnal mind and the spiritual man. _____

        _____

_____

_____.

4. Read James 1:22

    What are we to do when God speaks to us? _____

    _____.

5. Read Proverbs 3:5; Romans 9:1

    a. Why is excessive reasoning dangerous? _____

        _____

        _____.

    b. What three things does the human mind like? What is wrong
        with this? _____

        _____

        _____

        _____.

    c. How did Paul know he was doing the right thing and not rely-
        ing on his own reasoning? _____

        _____.

6. Read 1 Corinthians 2:1,2

    a. What was Paul's approach to reasoning? _____

        _____

        _____.

    b. Why is this a good example for us today? _____

        _____

        _____.

A Doubtful and Unbelieving Mind

1. Read Matthew 14:31; Mark 6:6

    What is the difference between the effects of doubt and unbelief? ___

    _____

    _____ .

2. Read 1 Kings 18:21; Romans 12:3 KJV

    a. How does the devil try to negate our faith?_____

    _____ .

    b. Why is it so important for us to know the Word of God? _____

    _____

    _____ .

3. Read Romans 4:18-21

    a. How did Abraham overcome the attack of Satan?_____

    _____

    _____ .

    b. What tools does Satan use to try to get us to "abort" our dreams? What do they both work against?_____

    _____ .

    c. Why does Satan attack us with doubt and unbelief? _____

    _____ .

    d. Why does the devil not want us to get our mind in agreement with our spirit?_____

    _____

_____

_____

_____ .

4. Read Matthew 14:24-32; Romans 4:18-21; Ephesians 6:14

   a. How were Peter and Abraham alike in their faith? How were they different?_____

   _____

   _____

   _____ .

   b. What are we to do in times of spiritual warfare?_____

   _____ .

   c. Why does Satan bring storms into your life?_____

   _____ .

   d. How do you resist him?_____

   _____

   _____ .

5. Read James 1:5-7

   Describe a time in your life when you were led by your heart rather than your head. _____

   _____

   _____

   _____ .

6. Read Matthew 21:18-22; John 14:12; Romans 12:3

   Faith is a gift from God; doubt is a _____ .
   Explain._____

   _____

   _____ .

7. Read Matthew 17:14-20 KJV; 11:28,29 KJV

   How does unbelief affect us?_____

   _____ .

8. Read Hebrews 4:11

   a. According to this Scripture, we as believers can enter _____ .

   b. The entire fourth chapter of the book of Hebrews speaks about
      _____ that is available to God's people.

   c. How does the Sabbath under the New Covenant differ from the
      Sabbath under the Old Covenant? _____

      _____

      _____ .

   d. How do we enter spiritual rest? _____

      _____ .

   e. How do we forfeit it?_____

      _____ .

9. Read Romans 1:17 KJV; Romans 15:13; James 1:7,8 KJV;
   2 Corinthians 10:5

a. How are the just (the righteous) supposed to live?_____
    _____ .

b. It is impossible to have joy and peace while living in _____ .

c. According to James 1:7,8 (KJV), what should we avoid doing in
    order to live the great life God has planned for us? _____
    _____ .

d. According to 2 Corinthians 10:5, what should we do instead? ___
    _____
    _____
    _____ .

An Anxious and Worried Mind

1. Read Psalm 37:8 KJV; Galatians 5:22; John 15:4 KJV; Matthew 6:25-34; Philippians 4:6; 1 Peter 5:7

    a. What are anxiety and worry? _____
    _____
    _____ .

    b. What is peace? _____ .

    c. How do we get the peace of God? _____ .

    Jesus said, "I am the Vine; you are the branches. . ." (John 15:5.) How long can a branch survive if it is broken off the vine? When we abide in Him, we enter the protection and rest of God. The life of abiding is a peaceful, restful and fruitful life. Enter in and enjoy your life while God works on your problems!

2. Read Matthew 6:25; John 10:10

    a. According to these verses, how is life intended to be? _____
    _____ .

    b. Why does Satan attack us with worry?_____ .

3. Read Matthew 6:25-30

    What does this passage of Scripture teach us about worry?_____
    _____
    _____ .

4. Read Matthew 6:31; 12:34 KJV

    The enemy knows that if he can get enough of the wrong things going on in our mind, what will eventually happen? _____
    _____ .

5. Read Matthew 6:32,33

    The world seeks after "things." What are we to seek?_____ .

6. Read Matthew 6:34

    Why shouldn't we spend today worrying about tomorrow?_____
    _____ .

7. Read Philippians 4:6; Hebrews 4:12; Ephesians 6:17 KJV

    The Word of God is our sword. Why must it be wielded against the enemy? _____
    _____
    _____ .

8. Read 2 Corinthians 10:5

    What is the single most effective weapon that can be used to win the war against worry and anxiety? _____
    _____ .

9. Read 1 Peter 5:6,7

    a. Why is a person who worries not a humble person? _____
        _____
        _____ .

b. What should our first response be in every situation? _____
_____ .

10. Read 2 Chronicles 20:12,15,17; John 14:27; Matthew 11:29; 6:34

a. What should our position be in adversity? _____
_____ .

b. There is no such thing as peace without opposition. Explain. __
_____
_____ .

c. How does being at peace, enjoying the rest of God in the midst of the storm, give glory to God? _____ .

11. Read Hebrews 13:5; Psalm 37:3

a. What is God letting us know in Hebrews 13:5? What has He promised in it? _____
_____
_____ .

b. What does Psalm 37:3 tell us about worry and how to handle it?
_____
_____ .

Chapter 13

A Judgmental, Critical and Suspicious Mind

1. Read Matthew 7:1 KJV

    a. What does it mean to judge others?_____
    _____ .

    b. Why is judging others wrong? _____
    _____
    _____ .

2. Read Romans 12:3

    a. Judgment and criticism are evidence of what deeper problem?
    _____ .

    b. What is the only reason we are able to excel in an area? _____
    _____ .

3. Read Galatians 6:1-3

    According to this Scripture, what mental attitude are we to maintain
    within ourselves? _____
    _____
    _____ .

4. Read Romans 14:4

    a. How can God help us with our weaknesses?_____
    _____ .

    b. Is it wrong to have a mental opinion of people? _____
    _____
    _____ .

    c. Why is it a major problem when we ponder over our opinion?

    _____

    _____ .

    d. How can the action of judging and criticizing be changed? _____

    _____ .

5. Read Matthew 7:1,2; Galatians 6:7

    How does the principle of sowing and reaping apply to the mental realm? _____

    _____

    _____ .

6. Read Matthew 7:3-5

    a. Why does the devil love to keep us busy, mentally judging the faults of others? _____

    _____ .

    b. Can we change others or ourselves? Why or why not? _____

    _____

    _____ .

7. Read Matthew 7:6

    How does this verse apply to judgment and criticism? _____

    _____

    _____ .

8. Read Romans 2:1

    a. How do we look at ourselves through rose-colored glasses but look at everyone else through a magnifying glass? _____

_____

_____ .

    b. How is a judgmental mind an offshoot of a negative mind? _____

_____ .

9. Read Proverbs 4:23

   Name two things that are "unthinkable" for a believer. _____

_____ .

10. Read 1 Corinthians 13:7

    a. What is the answer for a judgmental, critical, suspicious mind?

_____ .

    b. What does it mean to have a "balanced attitude"? _____

_____

_____ .

11. Read John 2:23-25; 1 Peter 5:8; 1 Corinthians 12:10 KJV

    a. What was Jesus' attitude toward His relationship with others?

_____

_____

_____ .

    b. Why do we need balance in human relationships? _____

_____ .

    c. What happens when we put our ultimate trust in God? _____

_____

_____ .

    d. What is the difference between suspicion and discernment?_____

_____

_____ .

    e. What does true spiritual discernment provoke? _____

_____ .

12. Read Proverbs 16:23,24; John 10:10

    a. What effect do our unspoken thoughts have on us?_____

_____

_____ .

    b. What will happen to us when we begin to operate in the mind of Christ? _____

_____

_____ .

Chapter

14

A Passive Mind

1. Read Hosea 4:6; 1 Peter 5:8; 2 Timothy 1:6

   a. What is "passivity" and why is it a dangerous problem? _____
   _____
   _____ .

   b. Why does the devil use passivity? _____
   _____ .

   c. How can a believer guarantee that the enemy will not win the
   war?_____
   _____
   _____ .

2. Read Ephesians 4:27 KJV; Luke 11:24-26

   a. Why is it dangerous to give Satan the "empty space" of our mind?
   _____
   _____ .

   b. Why doesn't casting down imaginations always work? _____
   _____
   _____ .

3. Read Romans 12:2; John 15:4,10 KJV; Matthew 5:27,28

   a. Explain this dynamic principle shown throughout God's Word:
   "right action follows right thinking." _____
   _____
   _____
   _____ .

b. Fruit comes as the result of what? _____

_____ .

c. What does this involve? _____

_____ .

d. What must a person do to get from wrong behavior to right
behavior? _____

_____

_____

_____ .

e. Why is it dangerous to "play around with sin" in the mind?___

_____

_____ .

4. Read Colossians 3:1,2

Explain the phrase, "You must have backbone and not just wish-
bone!" _____

_____

_____

_____ .

Chapter
15

The Mind of Christ

1. Read 1 Corinthians 2:16

   According to this Scripture, why is it possible for us to think as Jesus did? _____

   _____ .

2. Read Ezekiel 36:26,27; Romans 8:6; Amos 3:3

   a. Why did God give us His Spirit — a new nature, a new heart and mind — with the New Birth? _____

      _____ .

   b. What is the result of following the mind of the flesh? What is the result of following the mind of the Spirit?_____

      _____ .

   c. What is the first thing we must do in order to flow in the mind of Christ? _____

      _____

      _____ .

   d. What type of outlook and attitude did Jesus display?_____

      _____ .

   e. The mind of Christ in us is positive; therefore, any time we get negative, we are _____

      _____ .

   f. What is the dictionary definition of the word "depress"? How does this word apply to us?_____

      _____ .

3. Read Psalm 143:3-10

   a. What are the eight steps we can take to overcome depression?

   _____

   _____

   _____

   _____

   _____

   _____

   _____

   _____ .

   b. Give a description of someone who is depressed. _____

   _____ .

4. Read 2 Corinthians 10:4,5; Isaiah 26:3

   a. Why does Satan use depression? _____

   _____ .

   b. Where do negative feelings come from?_____

   _____ .

   c. What is the second thing we must do in order to flow in the
      mind of Christ? _____

   _____

   _____ .

5. Psalm 63:5,6; 77:12; 119:15; 143:5; 17:15

   a. If you want to experience victory, what will need to be a regular
      part of your thought life? _____

   _____ .

    b. What is the advantage of fellowshipping with God early each morning? _____

_____

_____ .

6. Read John 16:7; Matthew 28:20; Hebrews 13:5; 1 John 4:16

    a. Nothing is closer to us than _____ .

    b. Since God is always with us, how do we become conscious of His presence? _____

_____

_____ .

    c. What is the third thing we must do in order to flow in the mind of Christ? _____

_____

_____ .

7. Review 1 John 4:16, and read Romans 8:35,37

    a. How can we experience God's love for us? _____

_____ .

    b. What is the result of meditating on and confessing Romans 8:35,37? _____

_____

_____ .

8. Read 1 John 4:18 KJV; Romans 5:8 KJV

What is the result of righteousness-based thoughts? _____

_____ .

9. Read 2 Corinthians 5:21; Romans 12:8

    a. Why should thinking about guilt and condemnation be avoided?

    _____

    _____.

    b. What must we do instead of feeling guilt and condemnation?

    _____

    _____.

    c. What is the fourth thing we must do in order to flow in the mind
        of Christ? _____

    _____.

10. Review Romans 12:8, and read Ephesians 4:29; 1 Corinthians 13:7;
    Psalm 100:4

    a. Based on the ministry gift of exhortation spoken of in Romans
        12:8, what is exhortation?_____

    _____

    _____.

    b. What happens when you begin thinking loving thoughts about
        others? _____

    _____

    _____.

    c. Why do many people never see the answer to their prayers? ____

    _____

    _____

    _____.

   d. What is the fifth thing we must do in order to flow in the mind of Christ? _____

_____

_____ .

11. Review Psalm 100:4

   What is a sign that a person is flowing in the mind of Christ? ____

_____

_____ .

12. Read Hebrews 13:15; Psalm 34:1

   a. How can we be a blessing to the Lord? _____

_____ .

   b. Why is expressing appreciation so beneficial?_____

_____

_____ .

13. Read Ephesians 5:18-20; John 5:38

   a. How can we let the Holy Spirit ever fill and stimulate us?_____

_____

_____

_____

_____ .

   b. What is the sixth thing we must do in order to flow in the mind of Christ? _____

_____

_____ .

14. Review John 5:38

    a. According to this verse, what is God's Word? _____

    _____

    _____ .

    b. Why was it given? _____

    _____ .

    c. How is this accomplished? _____

    _____ .

15. Read Joshua 1:8; Psalm 1:2,3

    How do we put the Word of God into practice physically? _____

    _____ .

16. Read Proverbs 4:20-22

    The words of the Lord are a source of _____ and
    _____ to the flesh.

17. Read Mark 4:24

    How does the principle of sowing and reaping apply to this verse?

    _____

    _____

    _____

    _____ .

18. Read Mark 4:22

    Where does the power to do the Word of God come from?_____

    _____ .

19. Read James 1:21

    How does the implanting and rooting of the Word of God take place in our hearts? _____ _____ _____ .

20. Read Romans 8:6; Philippians 4:8; 2 Corinthians 10:5 KJV

    What do you achieve by continually "watching over" your thoughts?

    _____
    _____
    _____
    _____ .

PART 3

Wilderness Mentalities

Introduction

*T*he Children of Israel spent forty years in the wilderness making an eleven-day trip because they had a "wilderness mentality." We really shouldn't look at the Israelites with such astonishment because most of us do the same thing they did. We keep going around and around the same mountains instead of making progress. The result is that it takes us years to experience victory over something that could have and should have been dealt with quickly.

A wilderness mentality is a wrong mindset. We can have right or wrong mindsets. The right ones benefit us, and the wrong ones hurt us and hinder our progress. Colossians 3:2 teaches us to set our minds and keep them set. We need our minds set in the right direction because wrong mindsets not only affect our circumstances, but they also affect our inner life.

1. Read Deuteronomy 1:2

   Why was an eleven-day journey for the Children of Israel extended to a forty-year journey? _____
   _____
   _____ .

2. Read Deuteronomy 1:6

   a. How are we like the Israelites? _____
      _____
      _____
      _____ .

  b. What is God saying to us today that He said to the Children of Israel in their day? _____

  _____

  _____

  _____ .

3. Read Colossians 3:2

  a. What is a wilderness mentality? _____

  _____ .

  b. What should we do to avoid having a wilderness mentality? ____

  _____

  _____ .

  c. Why do we need our minds set in the right direction? _____

  _____

  _____

  _____ .

*"My future is determined by
my past and my present."*

Wilderness Mentality #1

1. Read Proverbs 29:18 KJV

   What was the Israelites' problem? _____

   _____

   _____

   _____ .

2. Read Luke 4:18,19 KJV

   When you face situations that are so bad it seems you have no real
   reason to hope, what must you remember? _____

   _____ .

3. Read Isaiah 11:1-3 KJV

   Can we judge things accurately by the sight of our natural eyes?
   Why or why not? _____

   _____

   _____ .

4. Read Numbers 14:2,3

   What was the attitude of the Israelites in this passage? _____

   _____

   _____

   _____ .

5. Read Numbers 20:2-4

   Where do such bad attitudes come from? _____
   _____ .

6. Read Numbers 21:4,5

   What other bad attitude of the Israelites do we see evidenced in this
   passage? _____
   _____
   _____ .

7. Read Genesis 13:7-11

   What was Abraham's attitude that allowed him to bless his nephew
   Lot in order to stay out of strife? _____
   _____ .

8. Read Genesis 13:14,15; Romans 4:17 KJV

   a. What was the result of Abraham's good attitude? _____
      _____
      _____
      _____ .

   b. In view of Abraham's situation, how should you think and speak
      about your future? _____
      _____
      _____
      _____ .

"Someone do it for me;
I don't want to take the responsibility."

Chapter

17

Wilderness Mentality #2

1. Read Genesis 11:31

    a. How is responsibility often defined? _____

    _____ .

    b. What does it mean to be responsible? _____

    _____ .

    c. How did Terah (Abram's father) respond to the opportunity God
        placed before him?_____

    _____

    _____ .

    d. How are we like Terah? Why do we respond that way? _____

    _____

    _____

    _____ .

2. Read Exodus 32:1-14, 30-32

    a. For what did the Israelites want to take responsibility? Who did
        it for them? How? _____

    _____

    _____ .

    b. As a parent, what does God want to teach His children? _____

    _____

    _____ .

3. Read Proverbs 6:6-11

   Why is it important to be motivated from within, not from without?

   _____

   _____

   _____ .

4. Read Matthew 20:16

   In regard to responsibility, the last part of this verse can be interpreted to mean that many are _____

   _____

   _____ .

5. Read Joshua 1:1-3

   If we are not willing to take our responsibility seriously and go forth to claim our spiritual inheritance, what will be the result? _____

   _____ .

6. Read Ecclesiastes 11:4

   a. How will meeting resistance to taking responsibility help you?

      _____

      _____ .

   b. What will happen if you only do what is easy? _____

      _____ .

7. Read Matthew 25:1-13

   According to verse 13 of this passage, what do we need to do while we are waiting for the Master's return? _____

   _____ .

8. Read Matthew 25:14-28; John 15:16

   a. How should you respond to the ability that God has placed in you? Why? _____
   _____
   _____ .

   b. What does the Bible clearly show us about God's will for us? __
   _____
   _____ .

9. Read 1 Peter 5:6,7 KJV

   a. What can we learn about care and responsibility from this chapter?
   _____
   _____ .

   b. What should you remember if God gives you whatever you ask Him for? _____
   _____
   _____ .

   c. Anyone operating in the mind of Christ will walk in _____
   — not _____ .

   d. Give a two-word summary of this entire chapter: _____
   _____ !

Chapter 18

"Please make everything easy; I can't take it if things are too hard!"

Wilderness Mentality #3

1. Read Deuteronomy 30:11

   Why aren't God's commands too difficult for us? _____
   _____
   _____ .

2. Read John 14:16

   a. When do things get hard? _____
   _____
   _____ .

   b. If everything in life were easy, what effect would it have on our lives? _____
   _____
   _____ .

   c. The Holy Spirit is in us and with us all the time for what purpose? _____
   _____
   _____
   _____ .

3. Read Exodus 13:17; Hebrews 4:16

   a. If you know God has asked you to do something, what should you do when things get hard?_____
   _____
   _____ .

b. Why did God lead the Children of Israel the long, hard way? __

_____

_____

_____ .

c. Did entering the Promised Land mean no more battles for the Israelites? _____

_____

_____

_____ .

d. Why did God lead the Children of Israel the longer, harder route even though there was a shorter, easier one?_____

_____

_____

_____ .

4. Read Galatians 6:9; Luke 4:1-13

a. Why is it important that we not give up in the mind, lose heart, grow weary and faint? _____

_____

_____ .

b. How was Jesus' forty-day fast in the wilderness different from the Israelites' forty-year wandering in the wilderness? _____

_____ .

5. Read 1 Peter 4:1,2

What secret concerning how to make it through difficult things and times does this passage teach us? _____

_____

_____

_____ .

6. Read Philippians 4:12,13 AMP; (in addition, read verse 13 in the *New King James Version*)

   a. What does right thinking do for us? _____

   _____ .

   b. If you are a whiner and a complainer, what should you do? _____

   _____

   _____ .

"I can't help it; I'm just addicted to grumbling, faultfinding and complaining."

Chapter

19

Wilderness Mentality #4

1. Read 1 Peter 2:19,20

   It is not suffering that glorifies God, but _____ .

2. Read 1 Peter 2:21-23

   How did Jesus endure suffering? _____

   _____

   _____

   _____ .

3. Read Ephesians 4:1,2

   To the many people in the world who are trying to find God, what is more important than what we tell them? _____

   _____ .

4. Read Psalm 105:17-19; Genesis 39-50

   Why was God eventually able to deliver and promote Joseph who was mistreated by his brothers and unjustly condemned to prison?

   _____ .

5. Read 1 Corinthians 10:9-11

   a. How was Joseph different from the Israelites? _____

      _____

      _____ .

b. What is the message of these passages of Scripture?_____

_____

_____ .

c. What was the difference between the Israelites and Jesus, our example?_____

_____

_____ .

d. What can we see in this contrast? _____

_____ .

6. Read Philippians 2:14,15

According to this passage, why are we to do all things without grumbling and faultfinding and complaining? _____

_____

_____

_____ .

7. Read Philippians 4:6

a. What does Paul teach us in this verse about how to solve our problems? _____

_____

_____ .

b. When does murmuring, grumbling, faultfinding and complaining usually occur in our lives? _____

_____

_____ .

c. What does the Word of God teach us to do during these times?

_____

_____ .

d. Patience is not the ability to wait, but _____

_____ .

e. How can you overcome complaining? _____

_____ .

Chapter 20

"Don't make me wait for anything; I deserve everything immediately."

Wilderness Mentality #5

1. Read James 5:7

   a. Impatience is the fruit of _____.

   b. Why should we learn to be patient while waiting? _____
   _____
   _____.

   c. What lesson do we need to learn about our life's journey? ____
   _____
   _____.

2. Read Romans 12:3

   a. Why does pride prevent waiting? _____
   _____
   _____.

   b. A humble person will not display an _____
   _____.

3. Read John 16:33

   a. If we get the idea in our heads that everything concerning us and our circumstances and relationships should always be perfect, what are we setting ourselves up for? How can this be stated another way? _____
   _____.

b. All the mishaps in the world cannot harm us if we will_____

_____.

4. Read Colossians 3:12

   a. How is patience described in this Scripture? _____

   _____

   _____.

   b. Why should we turn to this Scripture often? _____

   _____

   _____.

5. Read James 1:2-4; Galatians 5:22

   a. Patience is a fruit of the _____.

   b. According to the *New King James Version* of James 1, what is the method God uses to bring out patience in us? _____

   _____.

6. Read Numbers 21:4

   a. According to this Scripture, why did the Israelites become impatient, depressed and discouraged? _____

   _____.

   b. What will happen if you learn to respond patiently in all kinds of trials? _____

   _____

   _____.

7. Read Hebrews 10:36 AMP; 6:12 KJV

    a. Hebrews 10:36 tells us that without _____ and
        _____ we will not receive the promises of God.

    b. Hebrews 6:12 KJV tells us that it is only through _____
        and _____ that we inherit the promises.

8. Read Proverbs 16:25; John 6:63; Romans 13:14

    a. Why are there multitudes of unhappy, unfulfilled Christians in
        the world? _____
        _____
        _____ .

    b. When you are trying to wait on God, why does the devil pound
        your mind continuously demanding that you "do something"?
        _____ .

    c. Impatience is a sign of pride, and the only answer to pride is ____
        _____ .

9. Read 1 Peter 5:6

    a. What does the phrase "lower yourself in your own estimation"
        mean? _____
        _____
        _____
        _____ .

    b. What happens when we wait on God and refuse to move in
        fleshly zeal? _____
        _____

_____
_____ .

c. What should you do when you are tempted to become frustrated
and impatient? _____
_____
_____
_____ .

Chapter
21

"My behavior may be wrong, but it's not my fault."

Wilderness Mentality #6

1. Read Genesis 3:12,13

   Name one major cause for wilderness living. _____
   _____
   _____ .

2. Read Genesis 16:1-6 NKJV

   a. Give an example from your own life of blaming others. _____
      _____ .

   b. Why does Satan work hard on our minds — building strongholds
      that will prevent us from facing the truth? _____
      _____ .

   c. Why do we avoid facing the truth about ourselves and our behav-
      ior? _____
      _____
      _____ .

3. Read Numbers 21:5

   Have you ever gone around and around the same mountains in your
   life? What were your excuses? _____
   _____ .

4. Read Numbers 13:1-3, 25-28

   a. Who plants "ifs" and "buts" in our minds? How should we defeat
      this tactic? _____

_____

_____ .

    b. Name one reason our problems often defeat us. _____

_____ .

5. Read Psalm 51:1-6

What does verse 6 mean when it says that God desires truth "in the inner being"? _____

_____

_____ .

6. Read 1 John 1:8-10; Romans 3:20-24

    a. What must we do to truly repent? _____

_____ .

    b. Where is our justification found? _____

_____ .

    c. How are you and I made right with God after sinning? _____

_____

_____ .

7. Read John 1:1-5; 8:32

    a. What is one of the most powerful weapons against the kingdom of darkness? Why?_____

_____

_____

_____ .

   b. Jesus said it is truth that sets us free. How is the truth revealed?

_____

_____ .

8. Read John 16:12,13; Hebrews 13:5

   a. Who is "The Spirit of Truth"?_____

_____ .

   b. What is the major facet of His ministry to us? Why? _____

_____

_____ .

   c. What has God promised you to help you hang on to the truth about yourself?_____

_____

_____ .

   d. What is left for you to do now that you are on your way out of the wilderness?_____

_____

_____ .

"My life is so miserable; I feel sorry for myself because my life is so wretched!"

Wilderness Mentality #7

1. Read Numbers 14:1,2

    a. How did the Israelites react to their situation? _____

    _____

    _____ .

    b. What was God's word about such "pity parties"? _____

    _____ .

    c. What is vitally important to understand about this subject? _____

    _____

    _____ .

2. Read 1 Thessalonians 5:11

    a. What does the devil do the minute someone hurts us, the moment
        we experience disappointment? _____

    _____

    _____ .

    b. What will happen if you listen to the thoughts rushing into your
        mind during such times?_____

    _____ .

    c. How is self-pity perverted? _____

    _____

    _____ .

d. What happens when we take the love of God meant to be given away and turn it in toward ourselves? _____
_____ .

e. What is self-pity? Why is it wrong? _____
_____
_____ .

3. Read Philippians 2:4

a. How do we stay out of self-pity? _____
_____ .

b. How is self-pity supported? _____
_____ .

c. How is self-pity a major trap? _____
_____ .

d. What rare privilege does a Christian have when he experiences disappointment? _____
_____ .

4. Read Isaiah 43:18,19

As soon as you feel your emotions starting to rise up, what can you do? _____
_____
_____ .

"I don't deserve God's blessings because I am not worthy."

Wilderness Mentality #8

1. Read Joshua 5:9; Romans 8:17 KJV

   a. The Lord told Joshua that He had "rolled away" the reproach of Egypt from His people. What does the word "reproach" mean?

   _____ .

   b. God wants to give us grace. What does Satan want to give us?

   _____

   _____

   _____ .

   c. What does God's rolling away the reproach from us mean? _____

   _____

   _____ .

   d. Although we know we don't deserve God's blessings, why do we receive them anyway? How do we get them? _____

   _____ .

2. Read Galatians 4:7

   a. Are you a son or a slave — an heir or a bond servant? _____

   _____

   _____

   _____ .

   b. What is the difference between an heir and a bond servant? _____

   _____

   _____

_____

_____ .

    c. What does experience with the world teach us? _____

       _____ .

    d. What is the result of this teaching? _____

       _____

       _____ .

3. Read Numbers 13:33

    a. Because of the reproach upon them, what kind of an opinion did the Israelites have of themselves? _____

       _____ .

    b. How does Satan try to give you a negative opinion of yourself?

       _____

       _____

       _____

       _____

       _____ .

    c. How is a poor self-image, an attitude of unworthiness and an "I-don't-deserve-God's-blessings" mentality spread from one generation to the next? _____

       _____

       _____ .

    d. God is willing to give you mercy for your failures if _____

       _____ .

       He does not reward the perfect who have no flaws and never

make mistakes, but _____

_____

_____ .

4. Read Hebrews 11:6

   a. Without _____ you cannot please God.

   b. No matter how many _____ you offer, it
      will not please Him if they were done to _____
      His favor.

5. Read Ephesians 1:4

   According to this Scripture, what does the Lord want for us? _____

   _____

   _____

   _____ .

6. Read James 1:5; Philippians 1:6

   a. What does James 1:5 teach us? _____

      _____ .

   b. If you desire to have a victorious, powerful, positive life, you can-
      not be negative about yourself. Instead of being negative, what
      must you do? _____

      _____

      _____ .

   c. In Philippians 1:6, what does Paul say about you? _____

      _____

      _____

_____

_____ .

   d. After reading this chapter, how should you think and speak about yourself?_____

_____ .

"Why shouldn't I be jealous and envious when everybody else is better off than I am?"

Wilderness Mentality #9

1. Read John 21:21,22

   Jealousy, envy and mentally comparing ourselves and our circumstances with others is _____ .

2. Read Proverbs 14:30

   a. How will envy cause a person to behave? _____
   _____ .

   b. Define *envy* and *jealousy.* _____
   _____
   _____
   _____ .

3. Read Luke 22:24-26

   Why is life in the Kingdom of God usually the direct opposite of the way of the world or the flesh? _____
   _____
   _____
   _____ .

4. Read Galatians 5:26; Proverbs 3:3,4 KJV

   a. Where does promotion come from for the believer?_____
   _____ .

   b. God will give us favor with Him and with others if _____
   _____ .

5. Read 3 John 2 KJV

   a. What should you do when you recognize wrong thought patterns beginning to flow into your mind?_____ _____ _____ _____ .

   b. Why is it better to be around for the long haul than to be a "shooting star"? _____ _____ _____ .

   c. If you have had a mental stronghold for a long time in this area, what should you do? Why? What will be the result? _____ _____ _____ _____ .

"I'm going to do it my way, or not at all."

Chapter
25

Wilderness Mentality #10

1. Read Psalm 78:7,8

   a. What two mindsets did the Israelites display during their years in the wilderness that caused them to die out there? _____ _____ .

   b. What does God demand that we learn? Why? _____ _____ .

   c. How are "stubborn" and "rebellious" described? Do either or both of them describe you?_____ _____ _____ .

   d. Why is it not enough to reach a certain plateau and think, "I've gone as far as I'm going to go"? _____ _____ .

2. Read 1 Samuel 15:22,23; Romans 5:17; Revelation 1:6 KJV; Ecclesiastes 12:13

   a. Why do many of God's children fail to "reign as kings in life"? _____ _____ .

   b. How is obedience related to respect and reverence? _____ _____ .

   c. If Solomon had so much wisdom, how could he have made so many sad mistakes in his life?_____

_____

_____ .

3. Read Romans 5:19 KJV

    a. Explain how your choice to obey or not to obey not only affects
        you, but multitudes of others. _____

        _____

        _____

        _____

        _____ .

    b. Obedience is a far-reaching thing; it _____

        _____ .

4. Read 2 Corinthians 10:4,5; Isaiah 55:8

    a. Our thoughts are what get us into trouble quite often. What must
        we do to avoid this problem? _____

        _____

        _____ .

    b. What should you do if what is in your mind does not agree with
        God's thoughts (the Bible)? _____

        _____ .

    c. Satan has launched a war. What is the battlefield? _____

        _____

        _____ .

    d. How will this book assist you to win that war? _____

        _____

        _____ .

Personal Reflection

1. What aspect of *Battlefield of the Mind* was most meaningful for you?

   _____

   _____

   _____

   _____

   _____ .

2. Has reading it changed any of the established mindsets you may have
   had?_____

   _____

   _____

   _____

   _____

   _____ .

3. Has it helped you in any areas of difficulty and if so, what are they?

   _____

   _____

   _____

   _____

   _____ .

Prayer for a Personal Relationship with the Lord

God wants you to receive His free gift of salvation. Jesus wants to save you and fill you with the Holy Spirit more than anything. If you have never invited Jesus, the Prince of Peace, to be your Lord and Savior, I invite you to do so now. Pray the following prayer, and if you are really sincere about it, you will experience a new life in Christ.

Father,

You loved the world so much, You gave Your only begotten Son to die for our sins so that whoever believes in Him will not perish, but have eternal life.

Your Word says we are saved by grace through faith as a gift from You. There is nothing we can do to earn salvation.

I believe and confess with my mouth that Jesus Christ is Your Son, the Savior of the world. I believe He died on the cross for me and bore all of my sins, paying the price for them. I believe in my heart that You raised Jesus from the dead.

I ask You to forgive my sins. I confess Jesus as my Lord. According to Your Word, I am saved and will spend eternity with You! Thank You, Father. I am so grateful! In Jesus' name, amen.

See John 3:16; Ephesians 2:8,9; Romans 10:9,10; 1 Corinthians 15:3,4; 1 John 1:9; 4:14-16; 5:1,12,13.

Answers

Answers

Part 1: Introduction

1. The mind is the leader or forerunner of all our actions.

2. Our actions are a direct result of our thoughts.

3. We will prove out in our experience "the good and acceptable and perfect will of God" for our lives.

4. By comparing our thoughts with the Word of God. Any thought that attempts to exalt itself above the Word of God we are to cast down and bring into captivity to Jesus Christ.

Chapter 1

1a. With strategy and deceit, through well-laid plans and deliberate deception.

1b. ". . .the father of lies and of all that is false" (John 8:44).

1c. He uses a cleverly devised pattern of little nagging thoughts, suspicions, doubts, fears, wonderings, reasonings and theories.

1d. He is willing to invest any amount of time it takes to defeat us.

2a. Areas in which we are held in bondage (in prison) due to a certain way of thinking. Through careful strategy and cunning deceit.

2b. (Your answer.)

2c. (Your answer.)

3a. We must get the knowledge of God's truth in us, renew our minds with His Word, then use the weapons of 2 Corinthians 10:4,5 to tear down strongholds and every high and lofty thing that exalts itself against the knowledge of God. These "weapons" are the Word of God, praise and prayer.

3b. By "abiding"(continuing) in it until it becomes revelation given by inspiration of the Holy Spirit.

3c. Praise defeats the devil quicker than any other battle plan, but it must be genuine heart praise, not just lip service or a method being tried to see if it works. Also, praise and prayer both involve the Word. We praise God according to His Word and His goodness.

4a. God has promised good news for the poor, release for the captives, recovery of sight for the blind, deliverance for the oppressed and acceptance, salvation and free favors for all.

4b.   Continue to study God's Word and act on the truth of His Word. Also, face the truth about themselves and their past as God reveals it to them.

5.   God will not allow us to be tempted beyond what we can bear, but with every temptation He will also provide the way out, the escape.

Chapter 2

1.   Powerful; creative ability. Our thoughts affect what we become. We cannot have a positive life and a negative mind.

2a.   Renewed, God-like thinking.

2b.   Tear down the strongholds that Satan has built in it, using the weapons of the Word, praise and prayer.

3a.   The help of the Holy Spirit.

3b.   It is a vital necessity. Without it there is no life.

4a.   Thoughts bear fruit. Think good thoughts, and the fruit in your life will be good. Think bad thoughts, and the fruit in your life will be bad.

4b.   Yes. A sweet, kind person does not have mean, vindictive thoughts. By the same token, a truly evil person does not have good, loving thoughts.

Chapter 3

1.   If necessary, an inch at a time, always leaning on God's grace and not on your own ability to get the desired results.

2a.   "When you pass through the waters, I will be with you . . . . When you walk through the fire, you will not be burned or scorched. . . ."

2b.   By going through and not giving up, knowing that God helps us make spiritual progress by being with us to strengthen and encourage us to "keep on keeping on" in rough times.

3a.   By renewing our mind to follow after the Spirit and not the flesh, purposely choosing right thinking.

3b.   Since our thoughts become our words, we must choose life-generating thoughts. When we do, right words will follow, and we will choose life.

4a.   They had a "wilderness mentality." We can avoid a "wilderness mentality" by getting our mind renewed and learning to choose our thoughts carefully.

4b.   "You must not quit, or give up until victory is complete and you have taken possession of your rightful inheritance." The same thing.

Chapter 4

1a.   Little by little.

1b.   Lest the "beasts of the field" increase among them.

1c.   Pride.

2.   We rejoice more when freedom comes. When we try to do something on our own, fail and then realize that we must wait on God, our hearts overflow with thanksgiving and praise as He rises up and does what we cannot do ourselves.

3a.   When a baby is learning to walk, he falls many, many times before he enjoys confidence in walking. However, one thing in a baby's favor is the fact that, even though he may cry for a while after he has fallen, he always gets right back up and tries again.

3b.   Through discouragement and condemnation. Remind him and yourself that you do not walk after the flesh but after the Spirit.

3c.   Depending on yourself.

3d.   Depending on God.

3e.   It simply means that you don't do everything right.

4a.   Discouragement destroys hope. Without hope we give up, which is what the devil wants us to do.

4b.   Use the weapon of the Word to tear down strongholds. Purposely think right thoughts, and go the extra mile and speak them aloud in your confession. Refuse to be discouraged or feel condemned if you make a mistake. Be patient with yourself!

Chapter 5

1.   Positive thoughts, full of faith and hope, produce positive lives. Negative thoughts, full of fear and doubt, produce negative lives.

2a.   No, it says that all things "work together for good" to those who love the Lord and are called according to His design and purpose.

2b.   We are not to fall apart. Instead, we are to be readily adaptable and adjustable.

3.   We should not allow the things that have happened to us to keep affecting our new life in Christ.

4a.   If Jesus had not gone away, the Holy Spirit, the Comforter, would not have come.

4b. He will convict us of sin and convince us of righteousness.

4c. He is well able to bring it to full completion.

5. By having a ready mind, open to the will of God for us, whatever that will may be.

6a. We realize that no matter how negative the circumstances may seem, God is able to overcome them.

6b. Hope. It keeps us steady in time of trial.

7a. God wants to be gracious to us, to show mercy and loving-kindness to us. Expect it.

7b. Anxious thoughts. By having a "glad heart."

8. Keep our tongues free from evil and our lips from guile (treachery and deceit).

Chapter 6

1. By doing what Philippians 4:6,7 KJV says: being careful for nothing; but in everything, by prayer and supplication, with thanksgiving, letting our requests be made known unto God so that the peace of God, which passes all understanding, may keep our hearts and minds through Christ Jesus.

2. By abiding in the Word of God, which is the Truth that sets us free. His Word will heal us and rescue us from the pit of destruction.

3a. God often gives us faith for things that our minds just can't always come into agreement with, things our minds cannot understand, so we must decide to believe. By praying in Jesus' name and by the power of His blood, coming against "mind-binding spirits."

3b. Ask God for wisdom; He will give it to us and will show us what to do.

Chapter 7

1. The precepts of God — His instructions and teachings. We will prosper and come to maturity.

2a. We will get from the Word of God what we put into it.

2b. They do not delve into the Word of God very deeply. As a result, they get confused about why they are not powerful Christians living victorious lives.

3a. By meditating on it, by pondering on it, by contemplating it, by rehearsing or practicing it in our thinking.

3b. We really do not expect to be experts at anything in life without a lot of practice, so why would we expect Christianity to be any different?

4a. Meditate on the Word of God day and night.

4b. By controlling their thoughts.

5a. Our sensual nature. The impulses of our flesh, the thoughts of our carnal mind.

5b. To make sure we are not thinking all the wrong things.

6a. He literally came through the problem by choosing to remember the good times of past days — pondering the doings of God and the works of His hands. In other words, he thought on something good, and it helped him overcome depression.

6b. It is the power of the Holy Spirit working through the Word of God that brings victory into our lives. But a large part of the work that needs to be done is for us to line up our thinking with God and His Word. If we refuse to do this or think it is unimportant, we will never experience victory.

7a. So that we may prove for ourselves what is the good and acceptable and perfect will of God, even the thing which is good and acceptable and perfect in His sight for us.

7b. God's way of thinking.

8a. Our thoughts affect our attitudes and moods.

8b. By deceiving them into thinking that the source of their misery or trouble is something other than what it really is. He wants them to think they are unhappy due to what is going on around them (their circumstances), but the misery is actually due to what is going on inside them (their thoughts).

8c. It can help you locate some of your problems and be on your way to freedom very quickly.

Part 2: Introduction

1a. "The thoughts (feelings and purposes) of His heart."

1b. A critical, judgmental and suspicious mind.

2. No. They have to be renewed.

3. No. As children of God, it is our privilege to cast all of our care upon Him.

Chapter 8

1a. The mind.

1b. The mind and the spirit work together.

2a. The Holy Spirit knows the mind of God. Just as a person's own spirit within him is the only one who knows his thoughts, so the Spirit of God is the only One Who knows the mind of God.

2b. To reveal to us God's wisdom and revelation.

2c. This wisdom and revelation is imparted to our spirit, and our spirit then enlightens the eyes of our heart, which is our mind.

2d. So we can understand on a practical level what is being ministered to us spiritually.

2e. The natural does not understand the spiritual.

3. In "a still small voice."

4. Both with his spirit and with his mind.

5. The spirit is speaking something, and the mind is given understanding.

6a. So it cannot be free and available to the Holy Spirit working through your own human spirit.

6b. It should be both peaceful and alert.

Chapter 9

1a. Mental attack from the devil.

1b. An undisciplined thought life, vitamin deficiency and extreme fatigue.

1c. A lack of comprehension indicates a lack of understanding; a lack of concentration indicates an inability to focus.

2a. "Don't lose your balance or get off track." A wandering mind.

2b. (Your answer.)

2c. By disciplining it and keeping it on what you are doing.

3a. It leaves a person in indecision, and indecision causes confusion. Wondering, indecision and confusion prevent an individual from receiving from God, by faith, the answer to his prayer or need.

3b. Believe.

Chapter 10

1. They keep us from receiving what we need from God.

2a. Because of wondering and reasoning.

2b. Trying to figure out the "why" behind something.

2c. If what He tells us to do does not make sense, we may be tempted to disregard it.

3a. Obedience in the spirit.

3b. (Your answer.)

4. Mobilize — not rationalize.

5a. We can reason and figure something out that makes sense to us, but what we have reasoned to be correct may still be incorrect.

5b. Logic and order and reason. It leads to choosing what is comfortable but which may be totally wrong.

5c. It bore witness in his spirit.

6a. He resolved not to rely on human philosophy or wisdom but to know nothing but Jesus Christ and Him crucified.

6b. Excessive reasoning is not normal for the Christian who intends to be victorious — the believer who intends to win the war that is fought on the battlefield of the mind.

Chapter 11

1. Doubt causes a person to waver between two opinions, whereas unbelief leads to disobedience.

2a. By attacking us with doubt.

2b. Then we can recognize when the devil is lying to us.

3a. He continued to be steadfast, praising and giving glory to God.

3b. Doubt and unbelief. The mind.

3c. He doesn't want our mind in agreement with our spirit.

3d. He knows that if God places faith in us to do a thing, and we get positive and start consistently believing that we can actually do it, then we will do considerable damage to his kingdom.

4a. Both faced and acknowledged circumstances which seemed impossible. Unlike Abraham, however, Peter allowed doubt and unbelief to press in on him, and as he did, he began to sink.

4b. Tighten the belt of truth around us.

4c. To intimidate you.

4d. By remembering that the mind is the battlefield and by making decisions based on your spirit rather than on thoughts or feelings.

5.   (Your answer.)

6.   Choice. The seed of faith was planted in our hearts by God. Doubt is the devil's warfare tactic against our minds. We choose to doubt or to keep on believing!

7.   It will keep us from doing what God has called and anointed us to accomplish in life. It will also keep us from experiencing the sense of peace that He wants us to enjoy as we find rest for our souls in Him.

8a. The rest of God.

8b. A sabbath rest.

8c. Under the Old Covenant, the Sabbath was a day of rest. Under the New Covenant, the emphasis is on spiritual rest.

8d. Through believing.

8e. Through unbelief and disobedience.

9a. By faith.

9b. Unbelief.

9c. Being double-minded or living in doubt.

9d. ". . . refute arguments and theories and reasonings and every proud and lofty thing that sets itself up against the [true] knowledge of God; and . . . lead every thought and purpose away captive into the obedience of Christ (the Messiah, the Anointed One)."

Chapter 12

1a. Attacks on the mind intended to distract us from serving the Lord.

1b. A fruit of the Spirit.

1c. By abiding in the vine.

2a. Of such high quality that we enjoy it immensely.

2b. To steal our life from us.

3.   There is nothing in life that we are to worry about. We are valuable to God. Worry is useless. God will take care of us and provide for us.

4.   The wrong things will eventually begin to come out of our mouth.

5.   The Lord.

6.   We should use the time God has given us for what He intended.

7. A sword in its sheath won't do any good during an attack. God has given us His Word — we need to use it!

8. The Word coming forth out of a believer's mouth, with faith to back it up.

9a. A person who worries still thinks that in some way he can solve his own problem. The proud man is full of himself, while the humble man is full of God. The proud man worries; the humble man waits.

9b. To lean on God and to enter His rest.

10a. It is one of abiding in Jesus and entering the rest of God.

10b. God's peace is a spiritual peace, and His rest operates in the midst of the storm — not in its absence. Jesus did not come to remove all opposition from our lives, but rather to give us a different approach to the storms of life.

10c. It proves that His ways work.

11a. We do not need to have our minds set on money, worrying how we are going to take care of ourselves, because He will take care of these things for us. Never to leave (fail) us or forsake us.

11b. Don't worry. "Trust (lean on, rely on, and be confident) in the Lord and do good; so shall you dwell in the land and feed surely on His faithfulness, and truly you shall be fed."

Chapter 13

1a. To condemn or sentence them.

1b. God is the only One Who has the right to condemn or sentence; therefore, when we pass judgment on another, we are, in a certain sense, setting ourselves up as God in their life.

2a. Pride.

2b. God has given us grace for it.

3. We must have a "holy fear" of pride and be very careful of judging others or of being critical of them.

4a. He is able to make us stand and to justify us.

4b. No, we cannot always prevent ourselves from having opinions, but we do not have to express them.

4c. It becomes explosive and has the ability to do a great deal of harm in the realm of the relationship as well as in the spiritual realm.

4d. By changing the mind.

5. We can sow and reap an attitude as well as a crop or an investment.

6a. That way, we never see or deal with what is wrong with us.

6b. We cannot change others; only God can. We cannot change ourselves either, but we can cooperate with the Holy Spirit and allow Him to do the work.

7. When we judge and criticize, we have taken the holy thing (love) and cast it before dogs and hogs (demon spirits).

8a. We make excuses for our own behavior, but when someone else does the same thing we do, we are often merciless.

8b. It thinks about what is wrong with an individual instead of what is right.

9. Judgment and criticism.

10a. A balanced attitude.

10b. To use wisdom and discernment in dealing with others, without looking at everyone with a negative, suspicious eye, always expecting to be taken advantage of by them.

11a. He was not suspicious of others, but knowing human nature, He did not trust Himself to them in an unbalanced way.

11b. If we go beyond wisdom, trouble will brew, and we will be hurt.

11c. We open the door for the Holy Spirit to let us know when we're crossing over the line of balance.

11d. Suspicion comes out of the unrenewed mind; discernment comes out of the renewed spirit.

11e. Prayer, not gossip.

12a. They affect our inner man, our health, our joy and our attitude.

12b. We will step into a whole new realm of living.

Chapter 14

1a. The opposite of activity. The Word of God clearly teaches that we must be alert, cautious and active — that we are to fan the flame and stir up the gift within us.

1b. He knows it will spell the believer's ultimate defeat.

1c. By moving against him, using his will to resist him.

2a. An empty, passive mind can easily be filled with all kinds of wrong thoughts.

2b. The empty space that is left must be filled up with right thinking.

3a. We will not change our behavior until we change our thoughts. Right thinking comes first, and right action follows. Right action or correct behavior is a "fruit" of right thinking.

3b. Abiding in the vine.

3c. Being obedient.

3d. He must be constantly renewed in the spirit of his mind, having a fresh mental and spiritual attitude. To do that, he must first change his thoughts — activating his mind and lining it up with God's Word and will.

3e. The way for sinful action is paved through sinful thoughts.

4. You must be active — not passive. Right action begins with right thinking. Don't be passive in your mind. Start choosing right thoughts.

Chapter 15

1. We have His mind — and a new heart and spirit.

2a. He knew that we would need them to heed His ordinances and walk in His statutes.

2b. Death. Life.

2c. Think positive thoughts.

2d. A positive outlook and attitude.

2e. Not operating with the mind of Christ.

2f. "To lower in spirits: SADDEN."[1] We regularly have the opportunity to think negative thoughts, but they will only press us down further.

3a. 1) Identify the nature and cause of the problem.
2) Recognize that depression steals life and light.
3) Remember the good times.
4) Praise the Lord in the midst of the problem.
5) Ask for God's help.
6) Listen to the Lord.
7) Pray for deliverance.
8) Seek God's wisdom, knowledge and leadership.

3b. "Dwelling in dark places as one who is long dead."

4a. To drag millions into the pit of darkness and despair.

4b. From negative thoughts.

4c. Be God-minded.

5a. Meditating on God and His ways and works.

5b. It is one sure way to begin enjoying life.

6a. Our own thoughts.

6b. By thinking about Him.

6c. Be "God-Loves-Me" minded.

7a. By meditating on it.

7b. A "conscious knowing" of God's love.

8. A righteousness-consciousness.

9a. Thoughts of guilt and condemnation are a waste of time and turn into action.

9b. Rebuke the devil and start going forward by thinking right thoughts.

9c. Have an exhortative mind.

10a. Saying something encouraging or uplifting — something that makes others feel better and encourages them to press on.

10b. You will find them behaving in a more lovable manner.

10c. They negate what they have asked for with their own thoughts and words before God ever gets a chance to work in their behalf.

10d. Develop a thankful mind.

11. He will find his thoughts filled with praise and thanksgiving.

12a. By letting His praise continually be in our thoughts and mouths.

12b. It is not only good for the other person, but it is good for us, because it releases joy in us.

13a. By speaking to ourselves (through our thoughts) or to others (through our words) in psalms and hymns and spiritual songs. In other words, by keeping our thoughts and words on, and full of, the Word of God; by offering praise at all times and for everything, giving thanks.

13b. Be Word-minded.

14a. A written expression of His thoughts, how He thinks about every situation and subject.

14b. So people could believe and experience all the good results of it.

14c. By meditating on it.

15. By first practicing it mentally.

16. Health; healing.

17. The greater the amount of time we put into thinking about and studying the Word of God, the more we get out of it.

18. The practice of meditating on it.

19. Through attending to it — by having it on our mind more than anything else.

20. You begin to take every thought captive unto the obedience of Jesus Christ.

Part 3: Introduction

1. They had a "wilderness mentality."

2a. Most of us do the same thing they did. We keep going around and around the same mountains instead of making progress. The result is that it takes us years to experience victory over something that could have and should have been dealt with quickly.

2b. "You have dwelt long enough on the same mountain; it is time to move on."

3a. A wrong mindset.

3b. Set our minds and keep them set.

3c. Wrong mindsets not only affect our circumstances, but they also affect our inner life.

Chapter 16

1. They had no positive vision for their lives — no dreams. They knew where they came from but not where they were going. Everything was based on what they had seen and could see. They did not know how to see with "the eye of faith."

2. Your future is not determined by your past or your present!

3. No. We must have spiritual "eyes to see" and "ears to hear." We need to hear what the Spirit says, not what the world says.

4. They had a negative, complaining attitude. They were ready to give up easily, preferring to go back to bondage rather than press through the wilderness into the Promised Land.

5. They are the fruit of bad thoughts.

6. They had a tremendous lack of gratitude.

7. He knew that if he acted properly God would take care of him.

8a. The devil could not keep the blessings of God from him. God gave him even more possessions than he had enjoyed before the separation, and blessed him mightily in every way.

8b. In a positive way, according to what God has placed in your heart, and not according to what you have seen in the past or are seeing even now in the present.

Chapter 17

1a. As our response to God's ability.

1b. To respond to the opportunities that God has placed in front of us.

1c. Instead of going all the way to Canaan with the Lord, he chose to stop and settle in Haran.

1d. When God speaks to us and gives us an opportunity to do something, many times, like Terah, we never finish what we start. We get into it and realize there is more involved than goosebumps and excitement.

2a. Nothing. Moses. He did their praying; he sought God for them; he even did their repenting when they got themselves in trouble.

2b. To accept responsibility.

3. God sees all and our reward will come from Him if we persist in doing what He has asked us to do.

4. Called or given an opportunity to do something for the Lord, but very few are willing to take the responsibility to answer that call.

5. We will never have the privilege of standing and ministering under God's anointing.

6a. You will build your strength.

6b. You will always remain weak.

7. Watch, give strict attention and be cautious and active.

8a. By doing all that you can with it. So that when the Master returns, you can not only give Him what He has given you, but more besides.

8b. It is God's will for us to bear good fruit.

9a. Not to be afraid of responsibility, to cast our care, but not our responsibility.

9b. There is a responsibility that goes along with the blessing.

9c. Wisdom; emotions.

9d. Be responsible!

Chapter 18

1. He gives us His Spirit to work in us powerfully and to help us in all He has asked of us.

2a. When we are trying to do them independently without leaning on and relying on God's grace.

2b. We would not even need the power of the Holy Spirit to help us.

2c. To help us, to enable us to do what we cannot do and to do with ease what would be hard without Him.

3a. Spend more time with Him, lean more on Him and receive more grace from Him.

3b. They were still cowards, and He had to do a work in them to prepare them for the battles they would face in the Promised Land.

3c. No. After they crossed the Jordan River and went in to possess the land of promise, they fought one battle after another.

3d. He knew they were not ready for the battles they would face in possessing the land. He took them the harder way to teach them Who He was and that they could not depend on themselves.

4a. If we hold on, we will eventually reap.

4b. Jesus drew strength from His heavenly Father and came out in victory.

5. "Think about everything Jesus went through and how He endured suffering in His flesh, and it will help you make it through your difficulties. Arm yourselves for battle; prepare yourselves to win by thinking on what Jesus did. . . ."

6a. It "arms" us for battle.

6b. Get a new mindset that says, "I can do all things through Christ who strengthens me" (Philippians 4:13 NKJV).

Chapter 19

1. A godly attitude in suffering that pleases Him and brings glory to Him.

2. Gloriously! Silently, without complaint, trusting God no matter how things looked, He remained the same in every situation. He did not respond patiently when things were easy and impatiently when they were hard or unjust.

3. What we show them.

4. He never complained, and he had a proper attitude in suffering.

5a. He did not complain at all, and all they did was complain about every little thing that did not go their way.

5b. The complaining of the Israelites opened a door for the enemy who came in and destroyed them.

5c. The Israelites complained and remained in the wilderness. Jesus praised and was raised from the dead.

5d. The power of praise and thanksgiving and also the power of complaining.

6. That we may show ourselves to be blameless and guileless, innocent and uncontaminated, children of God without blemish in the midst of a perverted and wicked generation, among whom we are seen as bright lights in the dark world.

7a. To pray with thanksgiving in every circumstance.

7b. When either something or someone has not gone the way we want it to, or when we are having to wait for something longer than we expected.

7c. Be patient.

7d. The ability to keep a good attitude while waiting.

7e. By making the most of the mind of Christ that is within you.

Chapter 20

1a. Pride.

1b. Waiting is part of life. We actually spend more time in our lives waiting than we do receiving.

1c. To enjoy where we are while we are on our way to where we are going!

2a. The proud person thinks so highly of himself that he believes he should never be inconvenienced in any way.

2b. Impatient attitude.

3a. A fall. Satan is setting us up for a fall through wrong thinking.

3b. Remain in the love of God, displaying the fruit of the Spirit.

4a. As tireless and longsuffering, and having the power to endure whatever comes, with good temper.

4b. To remind ourselves of what kind of behavior we should be displaying in all situations.

5a. Spirit.

5b. "Various trials."

6a. Because of the trials of the way.

6b. You will find yourself living a quality of life that is not just endured but enjoyed to the full.

7a. Patience; endurance.

7b. Faith; patience.

8a. They are busy trying to make something happen, instead of waiting patiently for God to bring things to pass in His own time and His own way.

8b. He wants to move you in fleshly zeal because he knows that the flesh profits nothing.

8c. Humility.

9a. It does not mean to think badly of yourself. It simply means, "Don't think you can solve all your problems on your own."

9b. There is a "dying to self" that takes place. We begin to die to our own ways and our own timing and to become alive to God's will and way for us.

9c. Begin to say, "Lord, I want Your will in Your timing. I do not want to be ahead of You, nor do I want to be behind You. Help me, Father, to wait patiently on You!"

Chapter 21

1. An unwillingness to take responsibility for one's own actions, blaming everything that is wrong or goes wrong on someone else.

2a. (Your answer.)

2b. The truth will set us free, and he knows it!

2c. It is painful.

3. (Your answer.)

4a. Satan. By keeping our eyes on God and not on the potential problem.

4b. We think they are bigger than God.

5. If we want to receive God's blessings, we must be honest with Him about ourselves and our sins.

6a. Face and acknowledge the truth about what we have done.

6b. Only in Jesus Christ.

6c. Only by the blood of Jesus — not by our excuses.

7a. Truth. Truth is light, and the Bible says that the darkness has never overpowered the light, and it never will.

7b. By the Spirit of Truth.

8a. The Holy Spirit.

8b. To help us face truth — to bring us to a place of truth. Because only the truth will set us free.

8c. "I will never leave you nor forsake you."

8d. Enjoy the Promised Land!

Chapter 22

1a. They felt exceedingly sorry for themselves. Every inconvenience became a new excuse to engage in self-pity.

1b. "You can be pitiful or powerful, but you cannot be both."

1c. We cannot entertain demons of self-pity and also walk in the power of God!

2a. He assigns a demon to whisper lies to us about how cruelly and unjustly we have been mistreated.

2b. You will quickly realize how the enemy uses self-pity to keep us in bondage.

2c. It is taking something that God intended to be given to others and turning it in on ourselves.

2d. It becomes selfishness and self-centeredness, which actually destroy us.

2e. Idolatry. It makes us only aware of our own selves and our own needs and concerns — and that is certainly a narrow-minded way to live.

3a. By looking at the other person's side and not just at our own.

3b. By thinking only of us and no one else.

3c. If we are not careful, we can actually become addicted to it.

3d. He can be re-appointed.

4. Pray, "Oh God, help me pass this test. I don't want to go around this mountain even one more time!"

Chapter 23

1a. "Blame . . . disgrace: shame."[1]

1b. Disgrace, which is another word for reproach.

1c. Each of us must receive for ourselves the forgiveness He is offering for all our past sins.

1d. We are joint-heirs with Christ. He earned them, and we get them by placing our faith in Him.

2a. (Your answer.)

2b. An heir is one who receives something other than by merit, as when property is passed down from one person to another through a will. A bond servant or laborer, in the biblical sense, is one who is weary from trying to follow the Law. The term denotes burdensome toil and trouble.

2c. We must deserve everything we get.

2d. By the time we are finished with the world, the reproach of it lies heavy upon us and definitely needs to be rolled away.

3a. A negative opinion.

3b. He fills your mind (if he is allowed to) with all types of negative thinking about yourself. He began early building strongholds in your mind, many of them negative things about you and about how other people feel about you. He always arranges for a few situations in which you experience rejection, so he can bring the pain of it back to your remembrance during a time when you are trying to make some progress.

3c. It is passed on from a parent to his children.

3d. You are willing to receive it. Those who put their faith and trust in Him.

4a. Faith.

4b. "Good works"; "earn."

5. That we should know that we are loved, special, valuable and that we should be holy, blameless and above reproach.

6a. To receive from God without reproach.

6b. Not look at how far you have to go, but at how far you have come. Consider your progress and remember Philippians 1:6.

6c. ". . . I am convinced and sure of this very thing, that He Who began a good work in you will continue until the day of Jesus Christ [right up to the time of His return], developing [that good work] and perfecting and bringing it to full completion in you."

6d. Positively!

Chapter 24

1. A wilderness mentality.

2a.   In a way that is callous and crude — even animalistic at times.

2b.   *Envy* is "the feeling of displeasure produced by witnessing . . . the prosperity of others."[1] *Jealousy* is "feelings of envy, apprehension, or bitterness"[2]; being fearful of losing what you have to another; resentment of another's success, arising from feelings of envy.

3.   Jesus taught things like (author paraphrases), "Many who are first will be last, and the last will be first" (Mark 10:31), "Rejoice with those who are blessed" (Luke 15:6,9 KJV), "Pray for your enemies, and bless those who mistreat you" (Matthew 5:44). The world would say that this is foolishness — but Jesus says it is true power.

4a.   From God and not from man.

4b.   We will do things His way.

5a.   Talk to yourself a little. Say to yourself, "What good will it do me to be jealous of others? It won't get me blessed. God has an individual plan for each of us, and I am going to trust Him to do the best thing for me. It isn't any of my business what He chooses to do for other people." Then deliberately and purposely pray for them to be blessed more.

5b.   "Shooting stars" rise quickly and get a lot of attention, but usually they are around for only a short period of time. Most of the time they fall as quickly as they arise.

5c.   Get a new mindset. Set your mind to be happy for others and trust God with yourself. It will take some time and persistence, but when that old mental stronghold has been torn down and replaced by the Word of God, you will be on your way out of the wilderness and into the Promised Land.

Chapter 25

1a.   Stubbornness and rebellion.

1b.   To give up our own way and be pliable and moldable in His hands. As long as we are stubborn and rebellious, He can't use us.

1c.   "Stubborn" is described as obstinate; difficult to handle or work with, and "rebellious" as resisting control; resisting correction, unruly; refusing to follow ordinary guidelines. (Your answer.)

1d.   We must be obedient in all things — not holding back anything or keeping any doors in our lives closed to the Lord.

2a.   Because of their stubbornness and rebellion.

2b. Without obedience, there is no proper respect and reverence.

2c. The answer is simple: it is possible to have something and not use it. We have the mind of Christ, but do we always use it? Jesus has been made unto us wisdom from God, but do we always use wisdom? Solomon wanted to go his own way and do his own thing.

3a. Your decision to obey God affects other people, and when you decide to disobey God, that also affects others. You may disobey God and choose to stay in the wilderness, but please keep in mind that if you now have or ever have children, your decision will keep them in the wilderness with you. They may manage to get themselves out when they are grown, but they will pay a price for your disobedience.

3b. Closes the gates of hell and opens the windows of heaven.

4a. Choose to examine our thoughts in light of the Word of God, always being willing to submit our thoughts to His thoughts, knowing that His are best.

4b. Cast down your own thoughts and think on His.

4c. The mind!

4d. It will assist you in casting down imaginations, and every high and lofty thing that exalts itself against the knowledge of God, bringing every thought into captivity, into obedience to Jesus Christ.

Personal Reflection

1. (Your answer.)

2. (Your answer.)

3. (Your answer.)

Endnotes

Chapter 15

[1] *Webster's II New Riverside University Dictionary,* (Boston: Houghton Mifflin Company, 1984), s.v. "depress."

Chapter 23

[1] *Webster's II,* s.v. "reproach."

Chapter 24

[1] W.E. Vine, *Vine's Expository Dictionary of Old and New Testament Words* (Old Tappan: Fleming H. Revell, 1940), Vol. II: E-Li, p. 37.

[2] *Webster's II,* s.v. "jealousy."

About the Author

*J*oyce Meyer has been teaching the Word of God since 1976 and in full-time ministry since 1980. Previously the associate pastor at Life Christian Church in St. Louis, Missouri, she developed, coordinated, and taught a weekly meeting known as "Life In The Word." After more than five years, the Lord brought it to a conclusion, directing her to establish her own ministry and call it *"Life In The Word, Inc."*

Now, her *Life In The Word* radio and television broadcasts are seen and heard by millions across the United States and throughout the world. Joyce's teaching tapes are enjoyed internationally, and she travels extensively conducting *Life In The Word* conferences.

Joyce and her husband, Dave, the business administrator at *Life In The Word,* have been married for over 35 years. They reside in St. Louis, Missouri, and are the parents of four children. All four children are married and, along with their spouses, work with Dave and Joyce in the ministry.

Believing the call on her life is to establish believers in God's Word, Joyce says, "Jesus died to set the captives free, and far too many Christians have little or no victory in their daily lives." Finding herself in the same situation many years ago and having found freedom to live in victory through applying God's Word, Joyce goes equipped to set captives free and to exchange ashes for beauty. She believes that every person who walks in victory leads many others into victory. Her life is transparent, and her teachings are practical and can be applied in everyday life.

Joyce has taught on emotional healing and related subjects in meetings all over the country, helping multiplied thousands. She has recorded more than 225 different audiocassette albums and over 100 videos. She has also authored 51 books to help the body of Christ on various topics.

Her "Emotional Healing Package" contains over 23 hours of teaching on the subject. Albums included in this package are: "Confidence"; "Beauty for Ashes" (includes Joyce's teaching notes); "Managing Your Emotions"; "Bitterness, Resentment, and Unforgiveness"; "Root of Rejection"; and a 90-minute Scripture/music tape titled "Healing the Brokenhearted."

Joyce's "Mind Package" features five different audio tape series on the subject of the mind. They include: "Mental Strongholds and Mindsets"; "Wilderness Mentality"; "The Mind of the Flesh"; "The Wandering, Wondering Mind"; and "Mind, Mouth, Moods, and Attitudes." The package also contains Joyce's powerful book, *Battlefield of the Mind*. On the subject of love she has three tape series titled "Love Is..."; "Love: The Ultimate Power"; and "Loving God, Loving Yourself, and Loving Others," and a book titled *Reduce Me to Love*.

Write to Joyce Meyer's office for a resource catalog and further information on how to obtain the tapes you need to bring total healing to your life.

To contact the author write:

Joyce Meyer Ministries
P. O. Box 655
Fenton, Missouri 63026

or call: (636) 349-0303

Internet Address: www.joycemeyer.org

Please include your testimony or help received from this book when you write. Your prayer requests are welcome.

To contact the author
in Canada, please write:

Joyce Meyer Ministries Canada, Inc.
Lambeth Box 1300
London, ON N6P 1T5

or call: (636) 349-0303

In Australia, please write:

Joyce Meyer Ministries-Australia
Locked Bag 77
Mansfield Delivery Centre
Queensland 4122

or call: 07 3349 1200

In England, please write:

Joyce Meyer Ministries
P. O. Box 1549
Windsor
SL4 1GT

or call: (0) 1753-831102

Books By Joyce Meyer

Secrets to Exceptional Living

Eight Ways to Keep the Devil under Your Feet

Teenagers Are People Too!

Filled with the Spirit

A Celebration of Simplicity

The Joy of Believing Prayer

Never Lose Heart

Being the Person God Made You to Be

A Leader in the Making

"Good Morning, This Is God!" Gift Book

JESUS – Name Above All Names

"Good Morning, This Is God!" Daily Calendar

Help Me – I'm Married!

Reduce Me to Love

Be Healed in Jesus' Name

How to Succeed at Being Yourself

Eat and Stay Thin

Weary Warriors, Fainting Saints

Life in the Word Journal

Life in the Word Devotional

Be Anxious for Nothing

Be Anxious for Nothing Study Guide

The Help Me! Series:
I'm Alone!
I'm Stressed! • I'm Insecure!
I'm Discouraged! • I'm Depressed!
I'm Worried! • I'm Afraid!

Don't Dread

Managing Your Emotions

Healing the Brokenhearted

"Me and My Big Mouth!"
"Me and My Big Mouth!" Study Guide
Prepare to Prosper
Do It! Afraid
Expect a Move of God in Your Life . . . **Suddenly**
Enjoying Where You Are on the Way to Where You Are Going
The Most Important Decision You'll Ever Make
When, God, When?
Why, God, Why?
The Word, the Name, the Blood
Battlefield of the Mind
Battlefield of the Mind Study Guide
Tell Them I Love Them
Peace
The Root of Rejection
Beauty for Ashes
If Not for the Grace of God
New: *If Not for the Grace of God Study Guide*

By Dave Meyer
Nuggets of Life

Available from your local bookstore.

Harrison House
Tulsa, Oklahoma 74153
www.harrisonhouse.com

The Harrison House Vision

Proclaiming the truth and the power

Of the Gospel of Jesus Christ

With excellence;

Challenging Christians to

Live victoriously,

Grow spiritually,

Know God intimately.